Healthy Hearts Restoring Minds

The A-Z of emotional wellbeing

Sharon Platt-McDonald

This edition printed in 2010 by The Stanborough Press Ltd,
Alma Park, Grantham, Lincs., NG31 9SL.

British Library Cataloguing in Publication Data.

A catalogue record for this book is
available from the British Library.

ISBN 1-904685-81-1

Designed by Abigail Murphy

Printed in Thailand

Unless otherwise indicated all Scripture quotations are taken
from the *New International Version*®, Copyright © 1973, 1978,
1984 by International Bible Society. Used by permission of
Hodder and Stoughton Publishers.

Other scripture quotations, indicated by initials:
NKJV = *New King James Version* (Thomas Nelson)
MGE = *The Message* (NavPress)
KJV = *King James Version*

Profile

Sharon Platt-McDonald, MSc RHV RM RGN

Sharon Platt-McDonald currently works as the Health director and Special Needs co-ordinator for the British Union Conference of Seventh-day Adventists in the UK and Ireland. Her strategic role entails developing health programmes and teaching tools for local churches and communities and undertaking health presentations. As an author, editor and columnist, she regularly writes on health issues for church and community publications. Sharon is also a motivational speaker and health advocate. She is passionate about holistic health and the empowerment of individuals, enabling them to make lifestyle choices to enhance wellbeing.

'He has sent me to heal the broken-hearted,
to preach deliverance to the captives . . . to set
at liberty those who are oppressed.'
Luke 4:18, NKJV.

Introduction

Society today is a world on fast forward – full of complexities and ongoing challenges. Our lives sometimes feel out of control as we try to cope with the increasing pace and pressure of it all. We all need to take a moment for ourselves, to think about our wellbeing and the wellbeing of others, and enjoy the experience along the way.

None of us is exempt from the stress and strain of daily living. Life brings with it so many unexpected events and issues which can sometimes push us to our limit. Yet even as we are faced with these challenges we have the one constant, ever-present, faithful, unchanging God who has promised to be with us through it all. He tells us: 'Do not let your hearts be troubled . . . trust . . . in me.' John 14:1.

In spite of the many disappointments that life

sometimes brings us, there is always hope. Learning how to rest in God gives us a quiet heart; a heart that is 'still' to hear from him and respond accordingly and to see the hope he offers us. We rest from our anxieties, our hurts and our restlessness when we rest in God. I have been greatly encouraged by a favourite scripture of mine found in Psalm 46:10 which simply states: 'Be still, and know that I am God.' This has enabled me to look away from the distractions and problems of life and turn to God for help and reassurance.

Additionally, we are encouraged in Scripture to guard our minds. Consider the following verse which alerts us to resist the pressures of this world and focus our minds on the positive things God has for us.

'Do not conform any longer to the pattern of this world, but be transformed by the renewing of your mind. Then you will be able to test and approve what God's will is – his good, pleasing and perfect will.' Romans 12:2.

Much attention has been given to how to change one's lifestyle to obtain better health. However more attention needs to be directed towards modifying and changing the learned thinking habits that have created negative mindsets. In fact, research now demonstrates that lifestyle choices and changes become easier and more achievable when they are in sync with a positive mindset.

As you pause for a moment of reflection to read this book, take time to nurture both heart and mind. May you find within these pages snippets of wisdom, words of encouragement and nuggets of truth to empower, revitalise and stimulate you to keep pressing forward to achieve God's best for your life. Embrace the possibilities that lie before you, knowing that there is a divine plan for your existence.

Whatever has transpired in your past, whatever your present experience and whatever the future holds, may God grant you healing for yesterday, help for today and hope for tomorrow.

Sharon

'A person whose mind is quiet and satisfied
in God is in the pathway to health.'
E. G. White, *Mind, Character
and Personality, Vol. 2*, p.403.

Attitude

What are you thinking? Whatever your thoughts are, you begin to speak them to yourself. Your words, whether negative or positive, have the power to influence your life. Self-talk is extremely powerful because you believe what you hear yourself say.

Dale Carnegie was once asked, 'What is the biggest lesson you have ever learned?' He quickly replied, 'By far the most vital lesson I have ever learned is the importance of what we think. If I knew what you think, I would know what you are. Our thoughts make us what we are. . . .' Perhaps you have read the old maxim which states:

'Thoughts produce acts, acts produce habits, and habits produce character.'

This belief is closely reflected by the wisdom of the Bible and emphasises the power of the mind to translate what one thinks into actions, so, in effect, we act out our thoughts.

Proverbs 23:7 states: 'For as . . . [a man] thinks in his heart, so is he.'

The mind indeed is the measure of the man.

Try the following exercise to determine how you are thinking and how to recognise a positive attitude or negative mindset:

Positive thinking	Negative thinking
I am valued	No one values me
I am loved	I am not loved
I try to do the best I can	I make a mess of everything
If things go wrong there is always a way out	I am a failure I can't get anything right
I am able to take control if situations get challenging	I will never be able to move on from this
I can be happy	I won't be happy again
God is there for me	There is no hope for me

Fact:

Positive people remain healthier, have better relationships and achieve more than negative thinkers.

Action:

• Challenge your thoughts

• Be your own advocate by checking negative self-talk when you begin to criticise yourself

• Keep things in perspective and try to see the bigger picture

• Allow room for error

We need to make allowances when we get things wrong occasionally. We can learn from the mistake, take courage and move forward wiser for the next challenge.

Adversity

Managing negative life events is crucial to our emotional and mental wellbeing. How we handle present challenges can be a reflection of how we handled previous challenging life events. Sometimes we are hampered by the seeming failures of the past, rehearsing the difficulties and mistakes we encountered and allowing them to overshadow our present experiences. This can make current difficulties appear even worse than they actually are.

Focusing on the strength we can gain through Christ is key to survival when life deals us a cruel blow. We have his assurance that he does not leave us to struggle alone but tells us he will always be with us. In fact, he has assured us that we can trust him to handle whatever life brings us. He tells us in Hebrews 13:5: 'Never will I leave you; never will I forsake you.' This gives us confidence to face life's adversity and even make something good out of it. Every disappointment in life can be a stepping-stone to something greater, as long as we allow the Lord to show us the lesson in it and use it to equip us for the future.

Consider the following quote:

'With every adversity comes a seed of equal or greater opportunity.' Napoleon Hill.

God can turn what may seem to be to our detriment to our ultimate good. Romans 8:28 reminds us:

'And we know that in all things God works for the good of those who love him, who have been called according to his purpose.'

Action:

• When faced with a challenging life event keep things in perspective. Remember; this, too, will pass.

• Realise that you are not alone and God is there for you.

• Repeat Bible promises which give you encouragement.

Philippians 4:6-7 is one that reminds us to trust God in spite of the circumstances. It states:
'Do not be anxious about anything, but in everything, by prayer and petition, with thanksgiving, present your requests to God. And the peace of God, which transcends all understanding, will guard your hearts and your minds in Christ Jesus.'

Belief

Demonstrating the power of belief, the true story is told of the mixed-up X-rays.

Two men went to hospital to have a consultation as they had been experiencing uncomfortable symptoms over a period of time. Wanting to establish a diagnosis, they had each been referred to a specialist for consultation following a diagnostic X-ray. On arrival at the hospital the men's appointments had been placed one after the other, and their files placed in that order. As they were strangers, neither acknowledged the other as they took their seats and waited nervously to be called.

Following each X-ray an analysis of the pictures was taken. One X-ray demonstrated that one man was gravely ill and was not expected to live. The other X-ray, however, showed no evident problems and indicated that the man was in good health. While preparing each file for the appointments, an administrative error occurred and the X-rays were placed in the wrong files. The X-ray for the man who was healthy was put into the file of the man who was terminally ill, and the X-ray for the man who was terminally ill was put in the healthy man's file. Unfortunately, the mix up of the X-rays was not discovered prior to the appointment with the consultant.

The man who was gravely ill sat nervously in front of the consultant. From the X-ray in his file the consultant told him, 'I have good news for you. Your X-ray results show no problem at all. In fact, you are in good health. Go home and stop worrying.' Elated, the man went home and celebrated. Although physically he was dying, the impact of being told that there was nothing wrong with him and that his health was good ignited hope in him and immediately began to make him feel well. He went home and lived.

However, the man who was actually healthy was mistakenly given devastating news. The consultant gave him the diagnosis based on the wrong X-ray. 'I'm sorry,' the consultant said, 'I have bad news. Your X-ray shows that you are gravely ill and are not expected to recover. In fact, I have to inform you that you have only a short time to live.' The man was overwhelmed with grief, believing he was terminally ill. He went home in the belief that he was dying and began to feel very unwell. He shut himself away, became very depressed and lost interest in life. Shortly after that he died.

Fact:

• Beliefs affect your whole approach to life.

• Positive thoughts create positive feelings and ignite positive actions.

• Thoughts, feelings and beliefs can be altered, depending on the choices you make to embrace the positive or the negatives in life.

Action:

• Keep a 'thought' diary. This will enable you to identify your trends of thought and track your associated feelings and beliefs. It will help you to understand why you are having these negative thoughts and assist you in gaining more control over your thinking process and its impact.

• Identify your thoughts.

• Rethink your thinking. Gain a more positive outlook. Be realistic.

• Keep things in perspective.

'Anxiety in the heart of man causes depression, but a good word makes it glad.' Proverbs 12:25, NKJV.

Change

Life consists of natural stages where we go through a transition from one experience or event into another one.

Planning reflection time is one way of boosting your ability to deal with change when it comes. Thinking time enables you to examine the 'what ifs?' in life. However, no amount of preplanning or surmising can adequately prepare us for unexpected life events. When such changes occur we need to remember that God has an ultimate purpose for our lives and to be open to and flexible with what he permits. This is essential for your coping mechanism during times of transition.

I have now learnt to punctuate my daily existence with moments to pause and reflect on God, carving out quality time for myself and loved ones and having a positive mindset to life challenges.

'Do not be anxious about anything, but in everything, by prayer and petition, with thanksgiving, present your requests to God.' Philippians 4:6.

Action:
How to cope positively with change:

• Remember that God is still in control

• Analyse your beliefs

• Check your attitude

• Adjust your expectations

• Prioritise; set goals but break them up into mini steps

• Visualise the expected outcomes, but be flexible that things can change

- Think the expected outcome; live the expected outcome

- Be patient with yourself, others and circumstances

- Realise your limitations

- Recognise God is in charge

- Adopt a positive attitude

'Never be afraid to trust an unknown future to a known God.' Corrie Ten Boom.

Crisis

A life crisis can occur as a result of trauma, illness, broken trust or betrayal, redundancy, divorce, death or any other personal tragedy, and can result in the onset of depression or the further deterioration of damaged emotions.

One reassurance we have in times of crisis is that God is ever present and able to uphold us in our time of need.

If you identify with the following feelings, the Lord has a word for you:

Your feelings	Christ's response
Heaviness	'The garment of praise for the spirit of heaviness' Isaiah 61:3, NKJV.
Darkness	'Then your light will break forth like the dawn' Isaiah 58:8.
'I will never be happy again'	'The oil of gladness instead of mourning' Isaiah 61:3.
'I feel as if I'm slipping'	'He will not let your foot slip' Psalm 121:3.
'I feel as if I'm drowning'	'When you pass through the waters . . . they will not sweep over you' Isaiah 43:2.
Emptiness	'You were redeemed from the empty way of life' 1 Peter 1:18.
People condemn me	'Therefore there is now no condemnation for those who are in Christ Jesus' Romans 8:1.

Action:

• Following the crisis event, commit the issue to God and ask him to help you to cope stage by stage.

• If you find things too overwhelming to

tackle alone, ask someone to help you take action to sort out the practical issues which have arisen in order to assist you in gaining a sense of control.

• After the initial shock, it is advisable to talk through what has happened either with a trusted friend or counsellor in order to get a better perspective.

• Remember that a crisis is usually temporary and in time the pain of the event will diminish or even vanish.

• Try to establish what you have learnt from the crisis.

• Some people find that on the anniversary of a crisis event it is helpful to honour the memory in some way. However, it is important to end the day with a positive action to prevent negative emotions from overshadowing it.

Distress or De-stress?

Distress

The term *stress* originates from the word *distress*, whose Latin origin means 'to draw or pull apart'. This is indicative of the pressure individuals experience when under stress.

A stressful lifestyle can affect mental wellbeing by causing symptoms like poor memory, irritability, moodiness and depression, as well as having other negative repercussions on physical and spiritual health.

Action:
• Turn to God for help – 'In my distress I cried to the Lord, and he heard me' Psalm 120:1.

De-stress

A less stressful life ensures a healthy mind and body with a stronger defence against toxins that attack the body and negative thinking that affects the mind. Why not consider the following suggestions and include them in your daily life?

Action:

• Recognise when stress becomes destructive. Remember, some stress is necessary to motivate or inspire productivity.

• Recognise symptoms early. Too much stress (pressure that continues for too long and leaves you feeling out of control) can be harmful.

• Identify the cause as it helps you to work through the pressure.

• Write down in order of priority what stresses you and tackle each issue individually.

- Talk to a friend or counsellor; unloading helps.

- Accept what cannot be changed; it brings some relief.

- Try to avoid too many life-changing events in the course of a twelve-month period.

- Let go of resentment; it is toxic to the mind and induces stress.

- Confront un-forgiveness and anger in yourself and find time to address the root cause.

- Take time for rest and relaxation; it rejuvenates.

- Avoid junk food; it can aggravate stress symptoms.

- Maintain regular exercise to burn excess

adrenaline.

• Nurture your spiritual wellbeing. Spiritual health heals emotions.

• Increase your prayer life. Find a prayer partner with whom you can pray regularly.

• Learn to take one day at a time; don't look too far ahead as it can increase anxiety.

• Pace yourself. Don't try to fit too many tasks into a short timeframe.

• Practise saying 'no' so you can say 'no' to requests that put you under pressure.

• Enjoy the beauty of nature. Going for regular walks is one way to do this.

• Identify and enjoy more 'me-time' where you do something pleasant just for you.

• Spend time with positive people who help

to lift your spirit and make you laugh.

- Make a list of things you are grateful for; it helps to keep a positive perspective.

- Set life and personal goals but be mindful that life changes may cause a detour. Adaptability is the best response to combat disappointments.

Emotions

There are so many things that
affect the way we think or feel
about ourselves and others. In the
book *Mind, Character and
Personality*, E. G. White states:
'The mind needs to be controlled, for it has a
most powerful influence upon the health' (Vol. 2,
p. 681). The study of psychosomatic disorders
mirrors this quote. Numerous research studies
reveal the impact of the mind on the body.

Negative thinking

Psychoneuro-immunology – This is the study
of the effects of thought processes and their
impact on the immune system, leading to
disease. Negative thoughts and emotions flood
the body with hormones that depress the
immune system.

Positive thoughts and emotions

When we think positively and have a positive outlook on life, we release immune-enhancing hormones which have a beneficial effect on our body.

'A merry heart does good, like medicine, but a broken spirit dries the bones.' Proverbs 17:22.

Fact

Optimists tend to have happier lives and are healthier, regardless of the degree of stress they experience (Psychological Association's *Journal of Personality and Social Psychology* in 2002).

Several further studies have indicated that positive thinkers are more likely to stay healthy into middle age and have more successful careers than negative thinkers. Additionally they are 50% less likely to quit their jobs and 30 times more likely to be happy. Significantly, on average they add 7.7 years to their lifespan.

Action:

• Accentuate the positives.

• Create a Promise Box – This could contain a number of encouraging passages of Scripture which you can use as positive affirmations. Place it in strategic points in your home or carry in your handbag or briefcase.

• Affirmations are positive sayings which stimulate positive thoughts and foster confidence in times of challenge. Place affirmations around the house where you can easily see them or carry as inspiration cards.

• Take control of your emotions rather than letting them take control of you.

Emotional Wellbeing

Action:

• Try the following tips for promoting good emotional and mental health:

• Nurture your spiritual needs by factoring prayer and reflection time with God into your daily life. This may mean organising your schedule so that it is a priority and planning this special time ahead when you have a change to your daily routine.

• Spend time with people whose company you enjoy or those who are positive and upbeat.

• Do something positive for others on a regular basis.

• Give adequate time to fulfil your own needs.

• List the things that are troubling you.

• Prioritise your challenges on that list and deal with the ones that are easiest to deal with or the most stressful issue that you can give your immediate attention to.

• Deal with conflict.

• Get rid of resentment.

• Seek effective ways of dealing with stress.

• Manage anger.

• Foster forgiveness.

• Get adequate rest.

• Eat a balanced diet.

• Avoid caffeine, alcohol, tobacco and other non-prescription drugs.

• Engage in physical activities.

- Appreciate the beauty in nature.

- Undertake a fun or relaxing activity, for example, go for a scenic walk, listen to music, read a good book, watch a humorous video, talk to a friend and so on.

Fear

'For God has not given us a spirit of fear but of power and of love and of a sound mind.'
2 Timothy 1:7.

Fear is probably the most destructive tool that causes anxiety, self-doubt, phobia and paranoia. It saps your ability to see past hurdles and think positively about the present or have hope for the future.

Fear can sometimes come as a result of past failures or a sense of inadequacy.

We need to remind ourselves that just because things didn't turn out well before, it does not mean that this will be an ongoing pattern. As a reference point, it can highlight what went wrong so we can learn lessons and avoid the same pitfalls in the future. Don't let fear of failure hinder you from embracing the future with hope.

Author Ellen White reminds us:

'We have nothing to fear for the future, except as we shall forget the way the Lord has led us, and his teaching in our past experience.' (*Life Sketches*, p. 196.)

Action:

• Ask for God's help to get rid of any fear that may be keeping you in a negative mindset.

• Repeat Bible promises daily to focus you on God, his power and his promises for your life. As I thought about the fears I have overcome in my life and the impact of Scripture to combat them, I wrote down these words: 'A text a day keeps fear at bay.' I have proven this to be true.

• Use past failures as a reference point but

not as a guide.

• Philippians 4:13 is a therapeutic text for the mind: 'I can do all things through Christ who strengthens me.' (NKJV.) What a powerful affirmation! With Christ we are winners! Hold on to promises like this; it will boost your mental agility and drive fear away.

Food

Nutrition and emotional wellbeing are significantly linked. Insufficient magnesium, zinc and vitamin B6 (found in vegetables, fruit and pulses) have been linked to depression.

Depressed individuals may crave sugary and/or fatty foods during stress.

Excess amounts of sugars and refined foods can diminish thiamine, niacin, B12, magnesium and calcium. Reduced levels of these nutrients can increase nervousness, anxiety, fatigue, irritability and a nervous system response leading to increased stress sensitivity and a tendency to aggression.

Heart-healthy diets also contribute to the relief of depression.

Omega-3 fats have been suggested by research to have a calming and anti-depressive effect on the nervous system, enhancing brain health and mental wellbeing. Rich sources of omega-3 are flaxseeds, walnuts and almonds.

High-fibre diets improve mood and curb afternoon drowsiness. Foods rich in fibre include fresh fruits, vegetables, nuts and whole grains.

Experts in the field of stress management have identified the following key foods which aggravate stress reactions in certain people:

Action:

Avoid the following:

- High intake of refined sugars such as chocolate, cake, biscuits and sugar-based foods.

- High fat.

• Stimulants such as coffee or cola-based drinks.

• Saturated fat intake. Harmful saturated fats, including butter, whole milk, cheese, ice cream, red meat, palm, coconut and cottonseed oils. These raise the level of LDL cholesterol that can cause narrowing of blood vessels.

• Cholesterol. You can reduce cholesterol by avoiding egg yolks and organ meats (kidney, brain and liver).

Forgiveness

The head chaplain at the world-renowned Mayo Clinic defines forgiveness as a decision to let go of resentments and thoughts of revenge to untie yourself from thoughts and feelings about the offence committed against you.

Researchers at the clinic have undertaken studies which demonstrate that holding on to grudges can lead to health problems. Emerging research suggests that nursing a grudge can place the same physical strains on the body, such as tense muscles, elevated blood pressure, increased sweating and so forth, as a major stressful event. Additionally, psychological repercussions like resentment, anger, guilt and anxiety were more common in people who were unable to forgive.

Physical benefits of forgiveness
Among the health benefits of letting go of

hurts and resentments, researchers found forgiveness to be positively associated with five measures of health: physical symptoms, medications used, sleep quality, fatigue and somatic complaints.

Reduction in stress response: Research suggests a lowering of the stress response in individuals who readily forgive. This was evident in reduced muscle tension, fewer complaints of nervous symptoms, lessened palpitations and panic attacks.

Improved heart health: Studies have found that forgiveness is good for the heart. One study from the *Journal of Behavioural Medicine* found forgiveness to be associated with lower heart rate and blood pressure.

The pain impact: Studies on individuals with chronic pain demonstrated a reduction in pain symptoms in individuals who were more forgiving. One study highlighted people with chronic back pain reporting less pain and anxiety when they focused on converting anger to compassion.

Emotional benefits of forgiveness

Stanford researcher Frederic Luskin has studied the effects of forgiveness and defines it as 'the moment to moment experience of peace and understanding that occurs when an injured party's suffering is reduced by the process of transforming a grievance they have held against an offending party.'

Although more research is needed to evaluate formally the health benefits of forgiveness, a number of small studies have indicated some potential health benefits conferred by forgiveness. Results have suggested the following benefits:

- Improved conflict resolution

- Better recovery from trauma

- Decreased anger and negative thoughts

- Decreased anxiety

- Decreased depression and grief

- Decreased vulnerability to substance use

Spiritual benefits

'For if you forgive men when they sin against you, your heavenly Father will also forgive you. But if you do not forgive men their sins, your Father will not forgive your sins.' Matthew 6:14, 15.

Whenever we pray the Lord's prayer, we hold ourselves to account to forgive others. When we repeat the words in Matthew 6:12: 'Forgive us our debts, as we also have forgiven our debtors', we are asking God to offer us forgiveness in the same manner that we extend forgiveness to others. So, then, if we are unforgiving to others, we are literally telling God to treat us in the same way.

Forgiveness is related to love. When we forgive an individual we extend love to that person just as Christ extends love to us in his forgiveness of our sins. Forgiveness promotes inner peace, deepens our spiritual experience and makes us more Christ-like.

Fact:

• Identifying current feelings about past events gives you a starting point from which to assess where you are in the process of forgiveness.

• Negative emotions must be addressed and explored. This assists in the journey towards forgiveness.

• Holding on to hurts solidifies an unforgiving attitude.

• The act of forgiveness engenders health

benefits for mind, body and spirit.

Action:

Manage your feelings by doing the following exercises:

• Think of an incident that caused you distress or bring to mind the person who hurt you. Take note of the feelings the memory evokes. This is a good indicator of whether you are still upset or angry about the incident or the hurt that an individual caused you.

• Ask God to give you the desire to forgive.

• Try to convert the energy you expend in constantly rehearsing how unfair a challenging incident was into exploring ways of letting the hurt go. This may require professional help.

• Repeat Matthew 6:12 every time the memory of that negative incident or that person who hurt you comes to mind.

• Tell yourself every day that forgiveness is possible.

• Seek special prayer and/or counselling if you are struggling in this area.

To forgive yourself is a tonic to your heart and mind; to forgive others is a weight-lifting experience.

God

Life brings with it so many disappointments. Learning how to rest in God gives us a quiet heart; a heart that is 'still' to hear from him and respond accordingly. We rest from our anxieties, our hurts and our restlessness when we rest in God. I have been greatly encouraged by a favourite text of mine found in Psalm 46:10 which simply states:

'Be still, and know that I am God.'

This has enabled me to look away from the distractions and problems of life and turn to God for help and reassurance.

When we slow down the pace of life and stop our restless activity to be still with God, we are in a position to listen more effectively to him. Hearing God's voice is not so easy when we are rushing around, preoccupied with so many other things. No wonder we often find it hard to hear or know what God is saying to us about a given situation or issue or even have a sense of what his will is for our life.

When we acquire a true knowledge of God and his will for us, it helps us to be grounded in Christ, unmoved by the vicissitudes of life and secure in the peace that he gives.

Action:
• Today and every day dedicate some 'quiet time' to spend with God alone, to meet with him, to see, to connect, to feel and to experience him.

Gratitude

Gratitude is a super holistic healer. It has benefits for body, mind and spirit. Gratitude turns the tables on negative thinking, feeling sorry for yourself and a mindset that can't find anything in life to be thankful for. When we cultivate a grateful attitude we learn to appreciate and enjoy life more. It also motivates us to find a way around challenges as we give thanks that God is there to help us.

Research indicates a health boost when people live life with a grateful attitude. Happier people are healthier people both mentally and physically. The immune system is boosted by positive thinking and you become less susceptible to disease. Gratitude engenders a calmer approach to life, even in times of difficulty, as it keeps a positive perspective and allows us to think with clarity.

Action:

• Say 'Thank you' more often.

• Express your gratitude in positive actions and gestures. Note the response it has on the receiver and the satisfaction it gives you.

• Find something positive in your immediate environment to thank God for.

• Try practising the exercises in 'Savour the Senses' in the 'S' section of this book. This turns our thoughts towards God and encourages our thanksgiving to him for the world around us and the senses to enjoy it.

• Be aware of slipping into a complaining attitude and try to stop yourself in your tracks. If something needs improving, think of a way to make the situation better or at least try and minimise the negative impact.

• Practise praising and demonstrating

gratitude like the psalmist David when he said: 'I will bless the Lord at all times; His praise shall continually be in my mouth.' Psalm 34:1, NKJV.

• The following extract from Psalm 103:2-6 gives you a list of things to begin being grateful for.

'Praise the Lord, O my soul, and forget not all his benefits – who forgives all your sins and heals all your diseases, who redeems your life from the pit and crowns you with love and compassion, who satisfies your desires with good things so that your youth is renewed like the eagle's. The Lord works righteousness and justice for all the oppressed.'

Hurts and Hopes

One of the reasons for negative self-talk is the inability to get over the hurts of the past. When we hold on to the negatives and worries of our past, we cloud the present by nursing unhealed wounds and blight our future with the apprehension and fear of more pain to come.

Hurts

Life experiences and daily pressure can squeeze us into a mindset of negative thinking.

Many people live so much in the past that they cannot enjoy the present. Willie Jolley puts it this way: 'The past is supposed to be a place of reference, not a place of residence.' The past is past. Ask God to help you get over past hurts. Seek professional Christian counselling for hurts which exist from trauma and request ongoing prayer cover to assist you in this. Positive action and patient persistence will enable you to move past your hurts and embrace healing. Exchange hurt for wholeness.

Hopes

Using the word hope as an acronym, I have incorporated the following spiritual and emotional aspects as key elements to bring hope into our lives:

H – Healing

O – Outlook

P – Prayer

E – Encouragement

Action:

• Healing – List the area of pain that you are experiencing and ask God to administer his healing touch.

• Outlook – Check your perspective and vision for the future. Realise that with God your future is bright.

• Prayer – Get a prayer partner – someone whom you trust – to come alongside you in regular prayer sessions.

• Encouragement – Use Bible promises which speak to the particular area of hurt that you have encountered. Associate with positive individuals who encourage you to move forward instead of dwelling on the past.

The bridge between failure and success is hope. Choose to be hopeful today. It is the best self-motivator possible.

Inspiration

What or who inspires you?

Focusing on the positives in life can bring inspiration in itself:

Philippians 4:8 is an inspirational verse which focuses on the positive and gives us a prescription for good mental health:

'Whatever is true, whatever is noble, whatever is right, whatever is pure, whatever is lovely, whatever is admirable – if anything is excellent or praiseworthy – think about such things.'

• In times of adversity, God's Word is truly powerful. It infuses us with his truth, cancelling doubt and fear. We gain strength and courage for today and faith and trust for tomorrow.

• Every disappointment in life can be a stepping-stone to greater things, if we allow the

Lord to show us the lesson in it and use it to equip us for the future.

• Even if you have been diagnosed with a chronic illness, remember there is no diagnosis too hard for God to handle. Face your life with the conviction that with God all things are possible and rest assured that whatever you encounter in life God has a plan for you, and his plan is perfect.

Action:

• Commit to memory scriptures that will buffer you in difficult times.

• Think of the individuals in life who have suffered great tragedy but have emerged stronger and more successful as a result of facing their challenge positively.

• Tell yourself that if they made it through, so can you.

Junk and Jewels

Identify the positive things in your life. These are the jewels that you should treasure and hold on to. The junk is the negative stuff that drags you down or threatens your emotional wellbeing. These you need to eliminate as far as possible.

Both positive and negative things happen to each of us throughout our lives. We need to determine which ones we hold on to. When we ask God to intervene in our lives, he comes alongside us to strengthen us and give us discernment to make good choices.

Action:

• Detox your mind – The waste and toxins are the negative thoughts and the self-imposed limitations of your mind that poison your outlook on life and the way you see yourself. Select them and then press the delete button.

• Allow the Holy Spirit to filter your mind so that you can wash away all the negatives and replace them with positive thoughts – the goodness with which God intended to nourish you.

'. . . be transformed by the renewing of your mind. Then you will be able to test and approve what God's will is – his good, pleasing and perfect will.' Romans 12:2.

Knowledge

Knowledge is potential power; it is effective when you activate it. Knowing what works and acting on it enables focused action in times of change and challenge.

We need to draw on godly knowledge to guide us. Psalm 119:105 declares: 'Your word is a lamp to my feet and a light for my path.' When we seek godly wisdom through his Word, he will speak to us and show us the way.

As well as spiritual knowledge we also need practical information that will equip us emotionally and build resilience to keep our minds healthy. Research indicates that if we have cultivated good holistic health habits, it will enhance our ability to deal with life's crises.

Action:

The following are recommended brain boosters for emotional resilience:

• Pray daily – it enhances spiritual and emotional wellbeing.

• Drink 2 litres of water daily to boost brain function.

• Eat brain enhancing foods rich in B vitamins and omega-3 (see the section on food).

• Exercise your mind by reading one book a month, doing puzzles, watching documentaries or listening to a stimulating debate. This enhances brain efficiency by increasing the stimulation of specific parts of the brain.

• Reduce stress – it helps to preserve brain function and prevent premature ageing of the brain.

- Get adequate sleep – it helps to rejuvenate the brain.

- Enjoy family and social networks.

- Nurture a pet.

Laugh

Laughter helps the release of endorphins also known as 'happy hormones'. This gives a 'feel good' factor and lifts the spirit. A light spirit creates optimism, and optimism counters stress. Recent research studies have found that even pretending to be happy actually increases contentment.

Fact:

• A Dutch study published in 2008 found that those who were positive about the future and about relationships had a 55% less chance of dying early from all causes and a 23% reduced risk of heart disease.

• Pessimists lived an average twelve years less than optimists, according to American research. This is because negative people were more likely to suffer viral illnesses, thought to be due to lower immunity as a result of their negative thinking, and they were less likely to carry out self-checks for serious diseases such as cancer.

• Norwegian researchers found that those who laugh every day live an average seven years longer than the miserable.

Action:

• Associate with people who are light-hearted, enjoy having fun and who make you laugh.

• Don't take yourself too seriously.

• Learn to appreciate the lighter side of life.

M Monitoring Mindsets

Learning to slow down and pause from life's busy pace gives us a window of time to reflect on our thought patterns. Literally, we need to think about how we think. In doing so we can put our life experiences into perspective, have more time to reflect and discover who we are and check our reactions to life events. Monitoring our mindsets also allows us to find time for God and give over to him things that could otherwise weigh us down. This brings peace.

Action:

The following categories and questions are useful for self-analysis in gauging our mindsets:

Emotions – Do you have a general sense of wellbeing and contentment?

Attitudes – Do you have the resilience to be

able to deal with life's stresses and bounce back from adversity?

Do you experience a zest for living or have the ability to enjoy life, to laugh and have fun?

Life balance – Do you experience a sense of balance in your life – between work and leisure, solitude and sociability, sleep and wakefulness, rest and activity, exercise, and so on?

Do you see yourself as well-rounded – giving equal attention to mind, body and spirit?

Relationships – How easily do you care for yourself and others and enjoy positive relationships?

Prospective thinking – Do you look to the future with hope and see possibilities?

Self-realisation – Are you able to participate in life to the best of your ability, engaging in meaningful activities, pursuing your full potential?

Adaptability – How flexible are you to life's changing circumstances? Do you have the ability to adapt, grow and cope with a range of feelings that accompany change?

Questioning our thoughts, actions and how we respond to life events enables us to keep a check on our emotions. We deal with varying feelings and emotions on a daily basis. Sometimes these are fairly easy to cope with and sometimes they become challenging. Analysing the way we feel and questioning our emotions is a good way to discern both positive and negative thoughts.

Networking

Who encourages you? These are the people you will need to support you in your difficult times. Who motivates you? These are the individuals you may turn to for inspiration in times of challenge.

You make significant links by associating with the right people. Linking with significant others prevents us from working in isolation and equips us with support along the way. Networking will help you as you take your next step towards your goal and navigate through the journey of life! It enables us also to learn from others, develop our vision and gain the skills we need to achieve our goal.

Action:
• Look for the good in others and come alongside people who can add something

positive to your life.

• Why not identify people who are already where you want to get to and make connections?

• Shadow individuals who have the expertise that you are trying to acquire.

• Socialise with people who inspire you. They help to keep you motivated and believing that whatever you want to achieve for your life is possible.

Opportunities and Obstacles

Opportunities

Amid the uncertainty of life come moments of breakthrough where opportunities open up for us. Opportunities act as catalysts to propel you towards your goal. John Maxwell made this statement: 'The winner looks at the work that needs to be done and says, "Here's a great opportunity – I'll do my part to make it succeed." '

Ask yourself: What am I doing to enhance the opportunities in my life to enable me to accomplish my goals successfully?

Think of what you are going to do with the opportunities that God has blessed you with. This opportunity is not only for you. It is also for others. C. D. Brooks puts it this way: 'God opens doors for us. We must enter, then allow ourselves to be used to open doors for others.'

May we in our lifetime display the words of Alma Bazel Androzzo when she wrote:

'If I can help somebody as I pass along then my living will not be in vain.'

Action:

• Write down the possibilities or opportunities that are open to you.

• Ask God to show you how to make best use of them for yourself and for the good of others.

Obstacles

Obstacles are those roadblocks which stand between you and your goal. Throughout our lifetime we often face obstacles and difficulties that obscure the beauty of life. It is at such times that the struggle to cope desensitises us to the blessings around us.

The road to success is strewn with challenges along the way. However, they are rarely insurmountable because God always provides an escape route and directions along the way to enable you to get around the obstacles. He promises us in Isaiah 30:21 'Whether you turn to the right or to the left, your ears will hear a voice behind you, saying, "This is the way; walk in it." '

Action:
• Ask God to be your guide and show you the way out.

• Assess your obstacles but in the context of reframing that experience in order to propel you forward.

• Why not make a list of the difficulties you are currently facing?

• Identify the steps you have taken to address them so far.

• Ask someone you know well to help you identify what you have done well and what you might need to improve on.

Prayer and Praise

'Instead of worrying, pray. Let petitions and praises shape your worries into prayers, letting God know your concerns. Before you know it, a sense of God's wholeness, everything coming together for good, will come and settle you down.' Philippians 4:6, 7, MGE.

When we pray, it solidifies our faith and trust in God. Faith is key to our survival in times of challenge, as it enables us to maintain a positive outlook.

One of my favourite quotes states: 'Faith enables us to see the invisible, hear the inaudible, believe the incredible, think the unthinkable, and do the impossible.' (Author unknown.)

When we praise, our life is filled with the joy

of the Lord. Praise strengthens us to face the battles of life. The Bible tells us in Nehemiah 8:10: '. . . for the joy of the Lord is your strength'.

Praise is a weapon that defeats the enemy who tries to steal our joy.

Both prayer and praise strengthen our emotional and spiritual resolve.

Action:

• Make a list of all the things you would like to thank God for, then pray a prayer of thanksgiving to God about them.

• Prayer partnership – This provides prayer cover for you, particularly in times when you are experiencing challenges and find it difficult to pray. The realisation that someone is standing in prayer with you is both comforting and strengthening.

• Commit to memory songs of praise and thanksgiving to God. In a time of need these gems will reaffirm your faith, bring light amid the darkness of your trial and illuminate the path before you.

Pause for peace:

'Peace I leave with you; my peace I give you. I do not give to you as the world gives. Do not let your hearts be troubled and do not be afraid.' John 14:27.

'And the peace of God, which transcends all understanding, will guard your hearts and minds in Christ Jesus.' Philippians 4:7.

P.E.A.C.E. – a recipe for tranquil moments of reflection.

Action:

P – **Pause**. Stop and be still. Delight in the fact that you choose to 'be' rather than 'do' at this moment. Don't feel guilty about this time of seeming inactivity. Just enjoy it. Think of this time as a time of renewal where your energies are being replenished and you gain new strength to go again.

E – **Environment**. Retire to a treasured spot where you can easily unwind. Ensure that the lighting, the temperature and the furniture are comfortable and enhance a relaxing and reflective mood. Make this your personal area, a safe haven of retreat. You may wish to choose some appropriate music which adds to the ambience and aids your restful mood.

A – **Attitude**. Detox your mind. Getting rid of negative thoughts helps you to think more clearly and enhances general wellbeing. With a positive mindset you can face life with all its challenges, conquer the past with its disappointments and embrace the future with hope. Encourage yourself and others. It lifts your mood and reminds you of what is possible.

C – **Calm**. The ability to bring body, mind and spirit into a state of rest. Try a soothing herbal tea like chamomile, known for its calming properties, to relax the nerves and induce sleep. Prayer is a powerful exercise which releases the pressure and allows you to express hopes, hurts and joys. It enables you to connect with God, reflect and pace your thinking as you gain strength and wisdom to continue the journey of life.

E – **Exercise**. Engage in regular exercise; it's a great stress buster. Exercise improves the circulation, boosts immunity and maintains good health both mentally and physically. It also enhances rest.

Quest

What is your primary aim and goal in life? What is the key objective that drives you and to which you put all your energy and focus into achieving? What is your passion? Identifying your quest in life is important as it helps to give you a definite aim, something for which to strive. It fills you with vision and hope for the future. It ignites the flames of possibilities yet to be discovered.

The apostle Paul in a motivational speech told himself: 'I press on towards the goal to win the prize for which God has called me heavenwards in Christ Jesus.' Philippians 3:14. He had an aim, a goal, a purpose and he navigated a path towards it. Having a quest, a hunger and desire to achieve one's goal and life objective, enables us to progress and prevents us from being stagnated in life, watching others achieve along the way. Our quest also drives us to overcome hurdles along the way and keeps us positive.

Like Paul we have to motivate ourselves to the finish line. This journey called Life is never smooth sailing; it is always a press. Press past doubt, press past obstacles, press past the crowd, press past scoffers in your quest to reach your goal.

Action:

• Identify your life goals.

• Commit your desires and life objectives to God and seek his blessing but make sure he is leading you in that particular direction.

• Pursue these goals with confidence, knowing that God is alongside you.

Quit?

Quitting does not necessarily denote giving up. It can also refer to concluding something because it has consistently failed to work. This does not mean you have given up on life or on ever trying again. What is clear is that a decision has been made to close one door and look for the opportunity of another open door.

Action:

• Identify when it is time to stop, change direction or start over.

• Seek advice before taking the decision to end. You may require specialist advice or counselling.

• Remember to seek counsel from God.

'For by wise counsel you will wage your own war and in the multitude of counsellors there is safety.' Proverbs 24:6, NKJV.

R

Relationships

Our relationships with family and friends can have a profound impact upon our emotional wellbeing.

Family and friends

Significant others play an important part in our lives. Think of three important people in your life and analyse the impact they have had on you. Ask yourself what values and beliefs (negative and positive) they have passed on to you.

Family togetherness fosters the following:

• Emotional stability

• Good level of self-esteem

- Social development

- Secure relationships

- Higher chances of achieving life goals

You can't choose your family, but you can choose your friends. Avoid negative people who have a pessimistic outlook on life, drain you, and who are unappreciative.

Healthy friendships
- Avoid 'Job's comforters' – people who are ready to tell you want you did wrong or what you could have done better. This only increases the level of guilt and inadequacy that you might feel.

- Examine the friendships that have positive or negative influences.

- Identify who are the 'givers' and 'takers', the 'pushers' and 'pullers'.

The friend test

Think of three friends and apply the following questions:

- Who demands more of your time?

- Who adds to your life?

- Who gives you the most encouragement?

- Who do you encourage the most?

- How can you be a better friend to each of them?

Action:

- Associate with positive friends and loved ones on a regular basis.

- Create a network of caring people who will add to your life in a positive way. These can be found through faith-based communities, membership organisations, social clubs, special groups, activity centres, volunteer or statutory organisations. These associations engender good emotional wellbeing and will give you a wide-ranging support network in times of challenge.

Rest and Relaxation

In order of importance, rest may come low down on your list of priorities.

Our culture is results driven. Fuelled by industry's obsession with productivity and competitiveness, we are constantly being pushed to perform beyond our limits.

Indeed, our work life balance has been interrupted with the increasing demands of life and the pressure to do more.

In the gospels is recorded the advice Jesus gave his disciples. Returning from their preaching tour the twelve disciples were encouraged by Jesus to come away from the pressures of the day for a time of quality rest and relaxation. He took them aside for this time of renewal.

Mark 6:31 states: 'And he said to them,

"Come aside by yourselves to a deserted place and rest a while." ' (NKJV.)

Taking time for rest and relaxation allows us to pause from the treadmill of life. It is the renewal we need for body, mind and spirit.

Perhaps your life is bursting at the seams with activity and the juggling of work demands, family commitments and trying to find time with God. Take the advice Jesus offers, 'Come aside . . . and rest a while.'

Action:

• Put 'quiet time' on your agenda every day!

• Stress management is also key to relaxing and aiding good sleep.

• Increase physical activity to at least 30 minutes daily. Exercise releases endorphins (happy hormones) and inhibits the release of stress hormones like cortisol.

• Ensure that Sabbaths are a stress-free time. Remember it is a day when we rest from all our labours. This includes shelving our emotional baggage, avoiding too many meetings on the Sabbath and engaging in activities that enhance rest and reflection.

Savour the Senses

Take a moment to explore the blessings of our five senses. This gives us much to be thankful for and encourages a grateful heart which builds our emotional wellbeing.

Sight

Find a place of beauty where you can appreciate the loveliness and wonder of Creation. Take in the boldness of colour, appreciate the varying hues; relish the diverse shapes, sizes and contours. Absorb the vast expanse of sky, sea and land and breathe a prayer of thanks for the gift of sight and the sense of joy that it brings.

Close your eyes and imagine the most beautiful, tranquil scene. Use this visualisation to fill your immediate world and allow yourself to escape whenever you are feeling stressed and need time out to connect with yourself and God.

Sound

Place your hands over your ears and block out as much sound as possible for at least one minute.

Release your hands and take note of the sounds around you. Imagine you are hearing the world for the first time and give thanks for the ability to hear.

Play your favourite piece of music, softly at first then as loudly as you can stand it. Note the contrasts and the impact it has on you.

Bring it back to a comfortable level and appreciate the beauty of the notes, the rhythm of the beats and the depth of the sentiments if words are being sung.

Smell

Think of your favourite aroma. Imagine that you are taking in that delightful scent and basking in the fragrance that it exudes. Let it waft over your entire being. As you inhale and exhale slowly, visualise yourself breathing in a fresh breath of air and exhaling all the stressors out of your life.

The next time you are exposed to that aroma, give thanks for the sense of smell and the delight it brings.

Taste

Imagine you have placed in your mouth the most tantalising, luscious and satisfying food item. As your taste buds spring into action and the salivary juices are released, savour the moment and take care to let the experience linger. Hold on to the succulent flavour and appreciate the fulfilment it brings you.

The next time you enjoy your favourite food, appreciate the ability to taste and the enjoyment you gain from it.

Touch

Think of your favourite fabric and relish the

feel of it against your skin.

Enjoy an embrace. Share plenty of hugs with loved ones and observe the pleasure they receive from it.

Treat yourself to a massage and absorb yourself in the varying strokes, sense the lightness and pressure of each movement over your body. Let your body totally relax as you yield yourself to the sensation of touch. You deserve some pampering time.

Self-esteem

The term self-esteem is used to describe how we feel about ourselves and the value we attach to ourselves as people. Negative thoughts and beliefs about ourselves can lead to low self-esteem which can affect how we feel and behave in every aspect of our daily life.

We sometimes expect more of ourselves than we would of other people. As a result, when we fall short of our own high expectations, we judge ourselves too harshly.

Negative thoughts and emotions stem from negative self-talk which is our inner dialogue. These are the thoughts we have about ourselves and the words we say to ourselves. Self-talk also influences our self-esteem. Our words, whether negative or positive, have the power to influence our life. Self-talk is extremely powerful, because we believe what we hear ourselves say. This is a biblical principle.

Matthew 12:37 states: 'For by your words you will be justified, and by your words you will be condemned.' (NKJV.)

Fact:

• It is not what others think about us that counts, it is what we think about ourselves.

• More people talk themselves into failure than into success.

• Some people use affirmations to encourage positive self-talk. Affirmations are positive statements we tell ourselves. A positive affirmation is a self-fulfilling prophecy.

Action:

• Realise that God sees you as special.

• Practise positive self-talk by using daily

affirmations which you say aloud.

• Reciting Bible promises and claiming those texts of Scripture for your life is one way of keeping a positive self-analysis.

• Don't try to compare yourself with others. Just realise that you are unique and valuable.

• Engage in activities which encourage you to help others. When you do something for another person, it helps to divert your thoughts away from yourself and get rid of self-pity.

• Make a list of as many things as possible that you are good at or have done well in the past. If you find it difficult to do this, ask a family member or friend to make a list for you. In moments when you are feeling inadequate, review this list again to remind yourself of your achievements.

Dress to boost your confidence. Wear an

outfit or clothes that make you feel good about yourself. Get a new hairstyle or wear a hairdo that looks good on you.

Sleep

Current research studies have revealed that brain function is significantly compromised due to lack of sleep. Additionally, when we consistently have a poor quality of sleep it affects our ability to deal with emotional challenges and cope with crisis events in life.

Action:

• Aim for eight hours a night.

• Develop a routine for going to bed and getting up.

• Create an optimum sleep environment by enhancing the ambience in the room to induce relaxation. Ideally this should include a comfortable room temperature, dimmed lighting and minimal noise.

• Try simple relaxation techniques and breathing exercises to promote natural sleep.

• Reduce napping during the day as much as possible to encourage better sleep at night. However power naps of up to ten minutes can be beneficial when tired midday or afternoon.

• If you are on medication, ask your GP/consultant if your current medication has the potential to interfere with sleep. Additionally, you could ask whether your medication could be safely taken earlier in the day.

• Avoid stimulants and caffeinated products like coffee, chocolate and tea, particularly towards the evening. Eliminate tobacco and alcohol use.

Time Management

Think about it. Each week brings us 168 precious hours. What do they consist of? We spend approximately 56 hours sleeping and recuperating; 40-50 hours earning a living; 28 hours for eating and personal duties. There are about 30-40 hours left to do what we wish. How are we spending them?

Our lives are a compact diary of dates, activities, expectations and demands on our time. We are continually pressured to be more productive so we find ourselves searching for more and more time to fit it all in. Consequently we end up with over-packed lives and stress in equal measure.

The Bible gives us a clear perspective about the value of time and what we should do with it.

There is also a call for recognising that everything in life has its time and place. Knowing when to do things and how to do them ensures that we make the best use of time – allowing us to achieve the appropriate results.

Effective time management is also about balance and giving adequate time for the varied activities of daily living. This includes the cycle of adequate rest, work, sleep, recreation, relaxation, activity, reflection and so on.

Action:

• Think about what you can realistically do in the given time span without putting yourself under too much pressure.

• Break down each task into manageable chunks, then address one area at a time.

• If you are working on several things at once, set realistic goals as to when each one can be completed. Monitor the time spent on each area to minimise panic at the last minute when you have not left sufficient time for that task.

• Sabbath is a special time. It brings with it the blessings of the three Rs. It's a time of *rest*, *reflection* and *rejoicing*. Make sure you spend sufficient time doing all three.

• Ecclesiastes 3:1 states: 'There is a time for everything, and a season for every activity under heaven.' Verses 2-8 identify the various activities and events in life that we engage in and knowing the right time in which to do them.

U-turns

What do you do when life events take you in the opposite direction to where your dreams were taking you? When life reverses on you, how do you respond? There are many surprises that we encounter in life, and experience teaches us to expect the unexpected. When life throws us the unexpected and the event is an unpleasant one, we need to go to God and ask him for wisdom and direction to navigate our route. We require wisdom to make right decisions and clarity to see the path ahead.

Life is 10% what happens to us and 90% how we respond to it. What we sometimes consider to be a detour or life taking us off our chosen path, if viewed positively, can be used to our advantage. It may be an opportunity to review our life plans, embrace new perspectives, try a new route or even review our priorities.

Although the things we have to face, whether planned or unplanned, may take us by surprise, God is never surprised. He has already made provision for us ahead of time to rescue and provide for us.

Action:

• Realise that God is ultimately in control. There is nothing that happens to us that he cannot use to his advantage and our greater good.

• When life presents us with the unexpected and threatens to shake the very core of our foundation, look to God for hope, help and healing, and seek reassurance from the Scriptures.

In difficult times the words of Romans 8:28 are of great comfort and assurance: 'And we know that in all things God works for the good of those who love him, who have been called according to his purpose.'

Vision and Victory

Vision precedes victory, for if you can see it, you can believe it, and if you can believe it, you can achieve it! Never underestimate the power of vision to open up the way for progression. In fact, visualisation enables you to bring the distant dream closer by observing what it could look like. As you picture the end result, the goal you are hoping for, it will give you a more definitive aim and make the possibility of its fulfilment more believable.

Whatever affects your vision affects your mobility; you become stagnated. Vision is a biblical principle for success. No wonder the wise man declares in Proverbs 29:18: 'Where there is no vision, the people perish.' (KJV.)

Don't worry that you may not have everything

at hand to enable you to accomplish your goal or feel that you are emotionally ready or in a place to make it happen. Take the first steps, and God will help you to do the rest.

Consider this quote:

'Throughout the centuries, there were men who took first steps, down new roads, armed with nothing but their own vision.' Ayn Rand.

As you visualise your goal, remember to look up to the One who is able to make your dream a reality.

Embrace the vision of the psalmist David when he wrote: 'I lift up my eyes to the hills – where does my help come from? My help comes from the Lord.' Psalm 121:1, 2.

'Man cannot aspire if he looks down; if he is to rise, he must look up!' Samuel Smiles.

Action:

• Visualise your goal, present it to God, write it down, pray over it, then take steps to put it into action.

Wellbeing

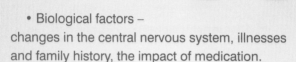

Mental wellbeing is generally influenced by two key areas:

• Biological factors –
changes in the central nervous system, illnesses and family history, the impact of medication.

• Social/environmental changes – and our emotional response to them – losses, traumatic events, stress and low economic status.

Achieving mental wellness is possible through:

• Spiritual nurturing

• Physical activity

• Good nutrition

- Adequate rest and sleep

- Stress reduction

- An optimistic attitude that can include humour, creativity and faith

- Emotionally enriched environments

- Medication management where necessary

Action:

- **Feed the spirit** – Prayer and meditation (silent reflection) have been shown to provide stress relief and resilience to face difficult life situations.

- **Move more** – A 2002 study found that exercise, particularly outdoors, was invigorating to both body and mind. The recommended exercise is five to six times a week. Building up gradually until you are exercising at 80% of your maximum heart rate is vital.

• **Eat well** – Omega-3-fatty acids found in flaxseeds, pumpkin seeds and walnuts or for non-vegetarians in oily fish like salmon. Omega-3 has been shown to improve mood. B vitamins, in particular B12, are excellent for maintaining the nervous system. Increase food rich in fibre, such as legumes, raw fruits, vegetables and oat bran.

• **Rest more** – Scientists have indicated that we need, on average, seven to eight hours' sleep a night to rejuvenate us holistically.

• **Enjoy music** – Listening to music that you enjoy has been found to be beneficial. A 2008 Cochrane review demonstrated that music enhances mood. In particular, for those who are depressed, music therapy was found to boost the emotional level so that they appeared to have fewer negative thoughts when listening to their favourite music.

• Monitor and manage medication –
Check with your healthcare professional about medication interactions. Inform your GP/consultant of all over-the-counter medications, vitamins, nutritional supplements, herbal remedies and teas that you take.

Worry

What a relief it would be to give worry a holiday! You could discover a whole new world of peace and wellbeing as you find new ways of easing life's pressures.

Don't think about what will be or what was; just think about what is. Love the present. Live the moment. Experience the 'now', and whatever comes next God will empower you to handle.

Just remembering that 'with God all things are possible' is enough to put our racing minds at ease as we remember that we are not alone and he equips us to do everything he has called us to do.

Action:

• Why worry when you can give it all to Jesus? He invites you not to share the load but to hand over all your anxieties and concerns to him. Do so. He is able to handle it. Repeat his promise to you on a daily basis: 'Casting all your care upon him, for he cares for you.' 1 Peter 5:7, NKJV.

X factor in your life

X is that extra 'something' that makes you unique. It is what defines you and makes you special. The X also stands for the special milestones that make us strive harder to reach our goals.

• You are eXtra special to God. He tells us: 'See, I have engraved you on the palms of my hands.' Isaiah 49:16.

• God has eXtraordinary plans for you. His words tell us: ' "For I know the plans I have for you," declares the Lord, "plans to prosper you and not to harm you, plans to give you hope and a future." ' Jeremiah 29:11.

• God has an eXciting future worth aiming for: He tells us: 'In my father's house are many rooms. . . . I am going there to prepare a place for you.' John 14:2.

Action:

• Make a list of the things that define you as unique.

• Thank God for the plans he has for you.

• Imagine what Heaven will be like and picture yourself being there.

You and your world

You are unique. There is so much in you that can impact your immediate world. God has gifted you with the potential to be the best that you can be.

How we view our immediate world is the sum total of how we look back on our past experiences, how we see our present circumstances and how we visualise our future prospects. Our lives are simply the overflow of our thoughts. Realising you are here for a purpose and that God believes in you will give you the determination to succeed.

Action:

• Take time to think. Spend time alone; just you and your thoughts. Relish the silence of the moment as you shut out the external and awaken your internal dialogue.

• Be aware of what you are thinking and the words you are using to describe who you are and the way you are feeling. Check that your self-analysis is gearing you in the direction of achieving your life's potential.

• Thank God for being there for you and for assisting you on this journey of life.

Zeal and Zest

Zeal

Think about what gets you up in the morning. OK, I know most people would state the necessity to work in order to pay all the bills! However, if you are to be truly satisfied and happy in life there needs to be something more to life than work and paying bills, unless of course your work is fantastic and the best thing in your life currently!

The *Penguin English Dictionary* defines *zeal* as: 'eagerness to accomplish something; ardent interest in pursuit of something'. Think of something that you have a passion for or desire to fulfil. Your zeal is the way you go about trying to accomplish that dream or desire. Look at the following words to ascertain whether you are experiencing zeal in any area of your life:

passion, fire, warmth, enthusiasm, eagerness, keenness, earnestness, intensity, vigour, energy, devotion. I hope you find at least one of those words applies to some aspect of your life.

Zest

Do you have a zest for life? If not, think about what it would be like to have your cherished dream or goal fulfilled, then live as if it were a reality. Have a long-term perspective on life, but be passionate about the immediate.

Ask yourself the question: 'What can I do today that will impact my future?' Do that one thing, and do it well. Then, as you accomplish today's purpose, tomorrow's goal will be realised as you pursue life with determination. As you undertake with zeal and passion the dreams that God has placed in your heart, you will enjoy the journey on the way to your destination.

With the realisation that God has given us life itself, we can give back to God lives that are abundant and full of the blessings and glory of God. Be rejuvenated; be transformed as you allow God to heal your heart and restore your mind.

Concluding thoughts

Having navigated your way through the pages of this book, take a moment to reflect on the journey. As you do so, I hope you are inspired to face your challenges with confidence, knowing that you are not alone and that you have the potential to succeed.

Step out with the assurance that God leads the way and that he will equip you to fulfil all that he has for your life. As you continue the journey, may you experience the healing he offers for your past, the help he gives for the present and the hope he extends for your future. I commit you to God, the healer of hearts and restorer of minds.

Sharon

'The Lord is my strength and my shield;
my heart trusts in him, and I am helped.
My heart leaps for joy and I will give
thanks to him in song.'
Psalm 28:7.

'O LORD my God, I called to you for
help and you healed me.'
Psalm 30:2.

'Heal me, O LORD, and I shall be healed;
save me and I shall be saved, for
you are the one I praise.'
Jeremiah 17:14.

' "I will restore you to health and heal
your wounds," declares the Lord.'
Jeremiah 30:17.

'Dear friend, I pray that you may enjoy
good health and that all may go well with you,
even as your soul is getting along well.'
3 John 2.

'He has sent me to heal the broken-hearted, to preach deliverance to the captives . . . to set at liberty those who are oppressed.'
Luke 4:18, NKJV.